SINCE 2021

Toronto, Ontario, Canada

TABLE OF CONTENTS

This book belongs to :

_____

_____

I am a symbol of elegance and grace,

With delicate flavors that embrace.

From the highlands where I'm grown,

My leaves are hand-rolled, a beauty to be shown.

I am a tea that's known for my hue,

A golden infusion, pleasing to the view.

Smooth and mellow is my taste,

Sip me slowly, and let time go to waste.

Hint: I share my name with a precious metal,

A tea that's cherished and truly special.

Who am I?

Answer: I am "White Tea."

I am a tea that's steeped in lore,

With a history that you can't ignore.

From the mountains, where clouds embrace,

I bring you flavors that leave a trace.

Leaves rolled into twisted shapes,

A process that no one can escape.

Dark and earthy, with hints of moss,

A distinctive taste, a captivating gloss.

Fermented and aged, I transform with time,

Developing complexity, a flavor so sublime.

A connoisseur's delight, sought by many,

A tea that's known as a true rarity.

Hint: I share my name with a color so deep,

A tea that's cherished, a secret to keep.

Who am I? "Black Tea."

I am a tea that's bright and clear,

Known for a taste that's light and dear.

With leaves rolled into tiny pearls,

A delicate infusion that unfurls.

Hailing from a land with ancient roots,

Where emperors sought its delicate shoots.

When steeped in water, I gracefully dance,

Releasing flavors that offer a trance.

A gentle aroma fills the air,

A sip of me is beyond compare.

Subtle sweetness with a hint of flower,

A tea that brings calm and quiet power.

Hint: My name starts with the letter "J,

A tea that takes you on a tranquil getaway.

Who am I? "Jasmine Tea."

In a tea that's loved by many,

With flavors that are quite uncanny.

Grown at high elevations, where air is crisp,

In a region known for its natural bliss.

Leaves hand-rolled into tiny balls,

Unfurling when hot water calls.

Green in color, with a fresh aroma,

A taste that's soothing, like a gentle coma.

With each sip, I bring vitality,

Boosting your health with much clarity.

Loaded with antioxidants, I must say,

A tea that keeps worries at bay.

Hint: My name is a homage to the place I'm from,

A tea that's cherished, a true kingdom.

Who am I? "Gunpowder Green Tea."

In a tea that's known for my allure,

A flavor profile that's quite pure.

From the land of dragons, I arise,

With legends that mystify and mesmerize.

Long and slender are my twisted leaves,

A brew that calms, a soul that relieves.

With a hint of sweetness and subtle earthy notes,

A tea that rejuvenates and uplifts spirits in boatloads.

Sip me hot or cold, as you desire,

A beverage that sets your taste buds on fire.

Cultivated with precision and art,

A tea that's cherished, a true work of heart.

Hint: My name starts with the letter "O,"

A tea that embodies elegance and tranquility.

Who am I? "Oolong Tea."

In a tea that's known for my allure,

A flavor profile that's quite pure.

From the land of dragons, I arise,

With legends that mystify and mesmerize.

Long and slender are my twisted leaves,

A brew that calms, a soul that relieves.

With a hint of sweetness and subtle earthy notes,

A tea that rejuvenates and uplifts spirits in boatloads.

Sip me hot or cold, as you desire,

A beverage that sets your taste buds on fire.

Cultivated with precision and art,

A tea that's cherished, a true work of heart.

Hint: My name starts with the letter "O,"

A tea that embodies elegance and tranquility.

Who am I? "Oolong Tea."

I'm a tea that's often overlooked,

But my taste is truly uncooked.

From a plant called Camellia sinensis,

I bring a flavor that's quite adventurous.

Not quite green, not quite black,

A tea with a taste that's right on track.

Somewhere in between, I reside,

With a character that cannot hide.

Grassy notes and a subtle bite,

A sip of me is a pure delight.

Refreshingly crisp, I'm light and clear,

A tea that's cherished by those who revere.

Hint: My name starts with the letter "Y,"

A tea that's often underestimated, oh my!

Who am I? "Yellow Tea."

I'm a tea that's a true delight,
With a flavor that's pure and bright.
Originating from a distant land,
I bring tranquility with a gentle hand.

My leaves are long, slender, and bold,
In water, their secrets slowly unfold.
A golden hue, like sunshine's gleam,
A cup of me is like a vivid dream.

Aromatic notes dance in the air,
A taste that's smooth, beyond compare.
With a touch of sweetness, so sublime,
A tea that transcends space and time.

Hint: My name is inspired by a mythical bird,
A tea that's cherished, like a whispered word.

Who am I? "Phoenix Oolong Tea."

I'm a tea that's prized and revered,

With a taste that's truly endeared.

Grown in a valley, nestled below,

Where cool mist and gentle breezes blow.

Leaves rolled into tight little balls,

Ready to unfurl when water calls.

Dark and mellow, with a touch of spice,

A brew that brings warmth, like a cozy device.

Hints of chocolate and caramel too,

Aroma that envelops, a scent that woo.

Velvety smooth, with a lingering charm,

A tea that soothes and offers calm.

Hint: My name starts with the letter "D,"

A tea that brings comfort, so heavenly.

Who am I? "Dian Hong Tea" or "Yunnan Black Tea."

I'm a tea that's shrouded in mystery,

With a taste that's steeped in history.

From the highest peaks, where clouds reside,

I bring you a flavor that's pure and wide.

Leaves handpicked with utmost care,

Crafted into bundles, beyond compare.

Sublime and delicate, like morning dew,

A tea that enchants with a brew.

Light and floral, with a subtle sweetness,

A flavor that brings moments of completeness.

A sip of me, a journey through time,

A tea that leaves memories sublime.

Hint: My name is inspired by a celestial body,

A tea that's treasured, unique and embody.

Who am I? "Moonlight White Tea."

I'm a tea that's hidden, quite unseen,

With flavors that make your senses keen.

Born in a valley, where rivers flow,

I bring a taste that's destined to grow.

Leaves tightly curled, like a secret embrace,

Unfolding gently, revealing their grace.

A deep crimson brew, with a bold embrace,

A tea that leaves an indelible trace.

Hints of fruit and sweetness intertwine,

Aroma enchanting, like a vintage wine.

Complex and layered, with every sip,

A tea that's cherished, in each tiny dip.

Hint: My name is like a ruby's hue,

A tea that's cherished by only a few.

Who am I? "Ruby Black Tea" or "Hong Cha."

I'm a tea from a sunny isle,

Where palm trees sway and waves beguile.

In azure waters, where I'm found,

A tropical delight that will astound.

Leaves that dance with vibrant zest,

Infused with flavors that are the best.

A symphony of fruits, a sweet medley,

A taste that's refreshing, oh so heavenly.

Tropical breeze carries my aroma,

A cup of me is pure Caribbean coma.

Golden in color, like the sun's rays,

A tea that brings warmth on island stays.

Hint: My name starts with the letter "H,"

A tea that brings the Caribbean your way.

Who am I?   "Hibiscus Tea."

I'm a tea that's known for my vibrant hue,
A color that's bold, a shade that's true.
Grown in a land with ancient roots,
I bring a flavor that simply suits.

Leaves that unfurl like a hidden treasure,
Revealing a taste that brings great pleasure.
A rich and earthy profile, it's true,
A tea that captivates, just for you.

With each sip, I transport you far,
To misty valleys where mountains spar.
A hint of smokiness, a touch of fire,
A tea that kindles warmth, higher and higher.

Hint: My name starts with the letter "L,"
A tea that brings the taste of legends to tell.

Who am I? "Lapsang Souchong Tea."

In a tea that's treasured, a true delight,

With a taste that shines in the darkest night.

From a country where dragons roam,

I bring you flavors that make your heart roam.

Leaves hand-rolled into little pearls,

Unfurling gracefully, a secret unfurls.

A floral aroma, like a gentle breeze,

A tea that brings you to serene seas.

Subtle and delicate, yet robust in taste,

A flavor that lingers, no time to waste.

Hints of orchids and a touch of sweetness,

A tea that fills your senses with completeness.

Hint: My name starts with the letter "J"

A tea that brings tranquility your way.

Who am I?   "Jasmine Dragon Pearl Tea."

I'm a tea that's celebrated, a true sensation,
With flavors that invite a sweet exploration.
Originating from a land of ancient tradition,
I bring you a taste that defies definition.

Leaves rolled into tight spirals so neat,
Ready to release their flavors, a treat.
A golden infusion, shining so bright,
A tea that brings you pure delight.

Hints of honey and a floral embrace,
Aroma that transports you to a serene place.
Smooth and velvety, a sip that enthralls,
A tea that's cherished within tea halls.

Hint: My name starts with the letter "D,"
A tea that's treasured, it's easy to see.

Who am I?   "Darjeeling Tea."

I'm a tea from a land rich and vast,

Where wildlife roams, a world so vast.

In golden plains, where the sun shines bright,

I bring you flavors that ignite delight.

Leaves plucked with care, by hands so skilled,

Crafted into a blend, a treasure fulfilled.

A taste that's robust, bold and grand,

A tea that's cherished across the land.

With hints of spices and a touch of heat,

Aroma that dances, a symphony complete.

An infusion that invigorates and inspires,

A tea that fuels your inner desires.

Hint: My name starts with the letter "R,"

A tea that represents Africa, from afar.

Who am I? "Rooibos Tea" or "Red Bush Tea."

In a land of passion and rhythm I reside,

Where salsa and samba set souls alight.

Harvested under the Latin sun's embrace,

I bring you flavor that dances with grace.

Leaves dark and bold, a taste that ignites,

Aromatic symphony that takes flight.

Steep me with passion, let your senses roam,

A cup of delight, a taste of home.

Hint: My name starts with the letter "Y,"

A tea from a Latin country, can you guess why?

Who am I? Yerba Mate

In a land of castles and rich history,

I am brewed with tradition and mystique, you see.

From rolling hills and picturesque views,

A beverage that captures the essence, I infuse.

Leaves carefully plucked from verdant gardens,

Processed with expertise, each step it hardens.

Aromatic notes dance upon the air,

A taste that transports you with utmost care.

Hint: My name starts with the letter "D,"

A tea beloved in a European country.

Who am I? Darjeeling Tea

From a land of mystique and fairy tale,
I come forth with flavor that will never fail.
Grown amidst fields of vibrant green,
My essence embodies a taste serene.

With golden hues and a delicate scent,
A sip of me brings moments of content.
Harvested with care, steeped to perfection,
A beverage that fills hearts with affection.

Hint: My name starts with the letter "C"
A tea cherished in a European country.

Who am I? Ceylon Tea, Beloved in Sri Lanka

In a land of vibrant culture and spice,
I offer a flavor that's incredibly nice.
From lush hills and verdant fields I'm derived,
A treasure of taste that keeps spirits alive.

Leaves hand-rolled with artistry and care,
Aromatic essence fills the air.
Steep me gently, watch the colors unfold,
A cup of joy, a story to be told.

Hint: My name starts with the letter "P,"
A tea celebrated in a country across the sea.

Who am I?

Pu-erh Tea (A fermented tea from China, known for its earthy flavor and centuries-old tradition)

From a land of rich cultural tapestry and beauty,

I come forth, a symbol of hospitality.

Grown on fertile soil, kissed by the sun,

My taste is a journey that's just begun.

Hand-picked and processed with utmost care,

Crafted into leaves with flavors rare.

A golden hue, a mesmerizing sight,

A cup of me brings warmth and delight.

Hint: My name starts with the letter "A"

A tea celebrated in a country far away.

Who am I?

Assan Tea (A robust tea from India, known for its strong flavor and popularity across the globe)

In a land of breathtaking landscapes and folklore,

I am born, a treasure to adore.

Nurtured by mist and cool mountain air,

I offer a taste that's beyond compare.

Leaves plucked by hand with love and precision,

Crafted into a drink that's a true vision.

Steeped in tradition, I hold ancient charm,

A sip of me brings comfort and calm.

Hint: My name starts with the letter "D,"

A tea celebrated in a country by the sea.

Who am I?

Darjeeling Tea (A prized tea from India, known for its delicate flavor and prestigious status as the "Champagne of Teas")

In a land of ancient wisdom and grace,
I'm treasured for my vibrant embrace.
Grown on misty hills with care and devotion,
I bring a flavor that sparks emotion.

Handpicked by skilled hands with precision,
Processed with artistry, a true fusion.
Deep crimson hue, enticing and bright,
A sip of me is a pure delight.

Hint: My name starts with the letter "R,"
A tea celebrated in a country afar.

Who am I?

Rooibos Tea (A South African herbal tea, known for its reddish color and naturally sweet tasted)

In a land of tropical beauty and rhythm,
In a tea that brings a taste sensation.
Harvested from leaves of an evergreen tree,
I bring a flavor that's loved by many.

With a touch of warmth and a hint of spice,
A sip of me feels like paradise.
Deep amber color, inviting and true,
In Caribbean culture, I'm known to brew.

Hint: My name starts with the letter "M,"
A tea cherished in a Caribbean melody.

Who am I?

Maté Tea (A traditional tea made from the leaves of the yerba maté tree, popular in countries like Argentina, Uruguay, and Paraguay, known for its stimulating properties and distinct flavor)

In the land of reggae and sun-kissed shores,
I'm a tea that offers delightful pours.
From the hills where cool breezes blow,
I bring a taste that makes hearts glow.

Harvested by skilled hands with care,
My leaves are steeped to create a flare.
A soothing blend of nature's own,
With every sip, my secrets are known.

Hint: My name starts with the letter "S,"
A tea cherished in island melodies.

Who am I?

Sorrel Tea (A popular herbal tea made from the dried calyx of the sorrel plant, commonly consumed in the Caribbean, known for its tart and refreshing flavor, often enjoyed during festive occasions)

Y	D	A	R	J	E	E	L	I	N	G	P	S	G	G	I	L
P	I	X	Z	D	Y	J	K	R	O	P	L	C	P	S	Q	S
Q	R	N	L	E	A	F	E	Y	G	O	T	L	X	P	N	O
K	O	M	N	A	O	R	T	L	A	T	L	N	W	O	U	Q
Z	A	A	U	T	R	D	T	P	U	W	K	O	T	U	Q	B
G	B	T	A	G	N	X	L	E	O	B	U	N	N	T	L	Q
X	V	S	Z	A	C	B	E	U	A	Y	A	S	M	G	Y	M
B	I	T	H	T	R	A	E	A	R	L	G	R	E	Y	U	X
Y	H	E	Q	R	Z	A	Z	G	P	E	N	O	D	U	H	S
R	Q	E	U	U	I	M	A	T	C	H	A	Z	R	B	N	E
P	O	P	V	A	S	S	A	M	N	L	I	P	G	I	H	N
C	N	O	R	T	Y	N	J	I	C	B	N	U	S	L	E	C
N	Y	J	I	J	W	H	A	R	Y	X	F	R	U	F	R	H
W	B	T	A	B	W	H	M	C	P	J	U	Z	G	C	B	A
B	A	R	X	J	O	V	I	U	U	G	S	L	R	H	A	H
E	Z	Q	E	A	Q	S	M	T	E	P	E	E	O	A	L	P
J	F	V	W	W	N	B	T	J	E	M	Q	L	L	I	S	E

- TEA
- POT
- CUP
- BREW
- STEEP
- SPOUT
- INFUSE
- LEAF
- MUG
- KETTLE
- SENCHA
- OOLONG
- DARJEELING
- ASSAM
- CHAI
- MATCHA
- EARLGREY
- HERBAL
- ROOIBOS
- WHITE

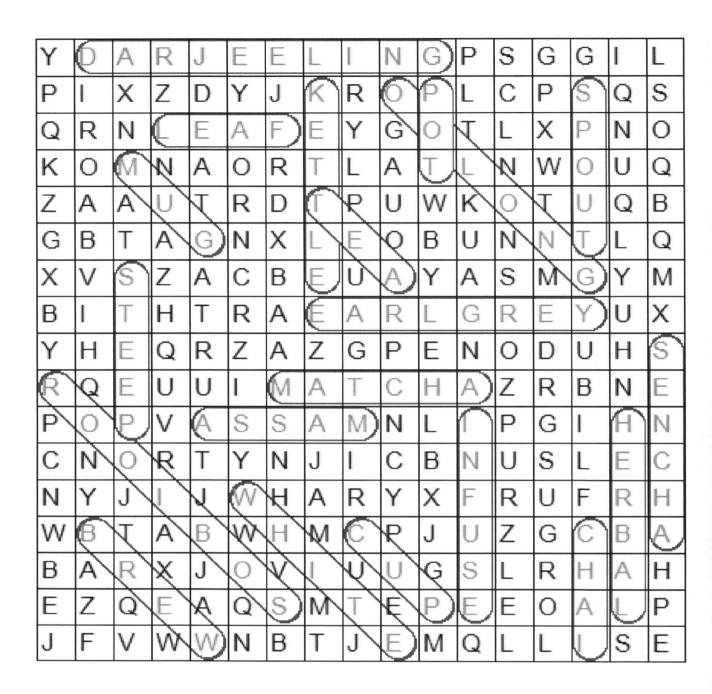

- TEA
- POT
- CUP
- BREW
- STEEP
- SPOUT
- INFUSE
- LEAF
- MUG
- KETTLE
- SENCHA
- OOLONG
- DARJEELING
- ASSAM
- CHAI
- MATCHA
- EARLGREY
- HERBAL
- ROOIBOS
- WHITE

1. The pleasant smell of brewed tea.
2. To prepare tea by steeping it in hot water.
3. A device used to hold loose tea leaves while steeping.
4. To drink slowly in small quantities.
5. A type of tea made from herbs, flowers, or other plants.
6. Another name for a teapot or a device used for steeping tea.
7. A type of ceramic material often used to make teapots and teacups.
8. An herbal tea or infusion made from dried herbs or fruits.
9. Having a pleasant and noticeable smell.
10. A traditional Chinese tea brewing method known for its precise preparation.
11. The part of a teapot from which the tea is poured.
12. A natural compound found in tea leaves that gives a bitter taste.
13. A stimulant naturally present in tea, known for its energizing effects.
14. A place where tea is served, often with a cozy atmosphere.
15. Informal term for a cup of tea.
16. A container with a spout, used for boiling water for tea.
17. A mixture of different types of tea leaves or flavors.
18. A Japanese teacup used in tea ceremonies.
19. To let tea leaves soak in hot water to extract their flavors.
20. A person who is addicted to or has a strong passion for tea.

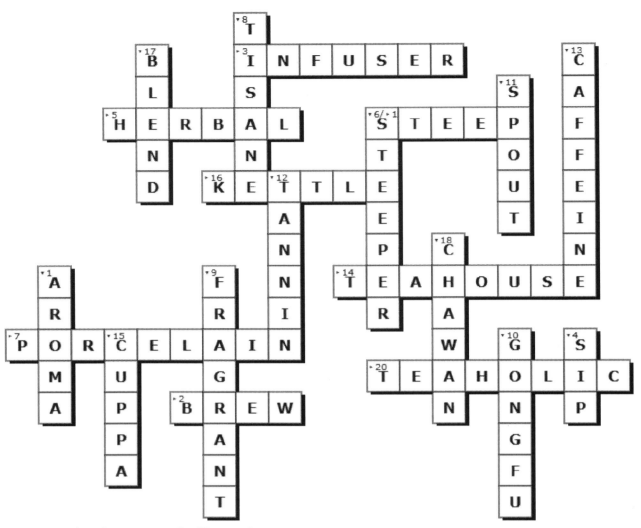

1. Aroma - The pleasant smell of brewed tea.
2. Brew - To prepare tea by steeping it in hot water.
3. Infuser - A device used to hold loose tea leaves while steeping.
4. Sip - To drink slowly in small quantities.
5. Herbal - A type of tea made from herbs, flowers, or other plants.
6. Steeper - Another name for a teapot or a device used for steeping tea.
7. Porcelain - A type of ceramic material often used to make teapots and teacups.
8. Tisane - An herbal tea or infusion made from dried herbs or fruits.
9. Fragrant - Having a pleasant and noticeable smell.
10. Gongfu - A traditional Chinese tea brewing method known for its precise preparation.
11. Spout - The part of a teapot from which the tea is poured.
12. Tannin - A natural compound found in tea leaves that gives a bitter taste.
13. Caffeine - A stimulant naturally present in tea, known for its energizing effects.
14. Teahouse - A place where tea is served, often with a cozy atmosphere.
15. Cuppa - Informal term for a cup of tea.
16. Kettle - A container with a spout, used for boiling water for tea.
17. Blend - A mixture of different types of tea leaves or flavors.
18. Chawan - A Japanese teacup used in tea ceremonies.
19. Steep - To let tea leaves soak in hot water to extract their flavors.
20. Teaholic - A person who is addicted to or has a strong passion for tea.

RELAX AND SIP

ACROSS

3. A popular baked treat often enjoyed with tea.
6. A spiced tea blend often made with black tea, milk, and spices.
7. A small cup used for drinking tea.
8. A portable container used for drinking tea on the go.
9. A type of black tea from India known for its floral aroma.
11. A partially oxidized tea with characteristics of both green and black teas.
16. Grey A type of black tea flavored with bergamot oil.
17. cozy A knitted cover used to keep the teapot warm.
18. strainer A tool used to separate tea leaves from the brewed liquid.
19. ceremony A formal ritualized way of preparing and serving tea.

DOWN

1. A robust black tea from India with a rich and malty flavor.
2. A place where tea is served, often with a cozy ambiance.
4. A refreshing way to enjoy tea on hot days.
5. A type of tea grown in Sri Lanka, known for its bright flavor.
10. A herbal tea from South Africa with a naturally sweet and nutty flavor.
12. A type of tea that undergoes minimal oxidation, resulting in a fresh and vegetal taste.
13. A common addition to tea, especially in British tea traditions.
14. A powdered green tea used in traditional Japanese tea ceremonies.
15. warmer A device or candle used to keep the teapot warm during serving.

RELAX AND SIP

ACROSS

3. A popular baked treat often enjoyed with tea.
6. A spiced tea blend often made with black tea, milk, and spices.
7. A small cup used for drinking tea.
8. A portable container used for drinking tea on the go.
9. A type of black tea from India known for its floral aroma.
11. A partially oxidized tea with characteristics of both green and black teas.
16. Grey A type of black tea flavored with bergamot oil.
17. cozy A knitted cover used to keep the teapot warm.
18. strainer A tool used to separate tea leaves from the brewed liquid.
19. ceremony A formal ritualized way of preparing and serving tea.

DOWN

1. A robust black tea from India with a rich and malty flavor.
2. A place where tea is served, often with a cozy ambiance.
4. A refreshing way to enjoy tea on hot days.
5. A type of tea grown in Sri Lanka, known for its bright flavor.
10. A herbal tea from South Africa with a naturally sweet and nutty flavor.
12. A type of tea that undergoes minimal oxidation, resulting in a fresh and vegetal taste.
13. A common addition to tea, especially in British tea traditions.
14. A powdered green tea used in traditional Japanese tea ceremonies.
15. warmer A device or candle used to keep the teapot warm during serving.

savor your tea time!

```
R E F I N E D Y V F O F W S F
X M C K G E P Z R P K T J E R
U J A P J U X U Z E I I R A
I S T E I H W L D C C N N E G
M E E I G R E V E E N D A N R
A T C O N N O I S S E U R I A
S V Z D C F R H J R D L O E N
D C R E E E U U P Z A G M T C
J B V Q V L K S T U C E A I E
O C G E Z G I K I S E N T S W
S J R S H N U C L O D C I I G
S O O T H I N G A G N E C U K
Z Y M M E D I T A T I V E Q Q
Y T I C I L P I S W E U O X P
Y T I L I U Q N A R T W X E F
```

Aromatic   Connoisseur   Decadence

Delicate   Euphoria   Exquisite

Fragrance   Indulgence   Infusion

Meditative   Opulence   Refined

Reverie   Sereni   Siplicity

Soothing   Steeped   tea

Tranquility

savor your tea time!

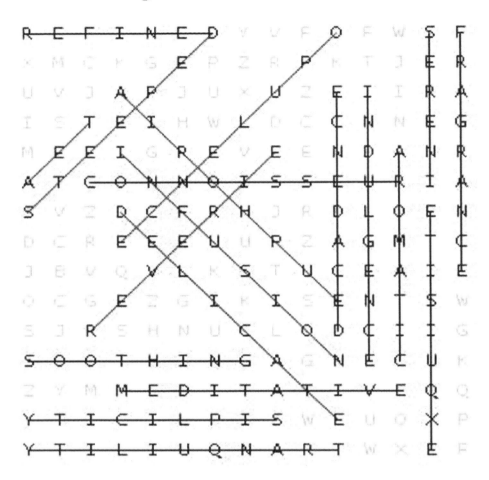

Aromatic   Connoisseur   Decadence

Delicate   Euphoria   Exquisite

Fragrance   Indulgence   Infusion

Meditative   Opulence   Refined

Reverie   Sereni   Siplicity

Soothing   Steeped   tea

Tranquility

"SIP IN BLISS"

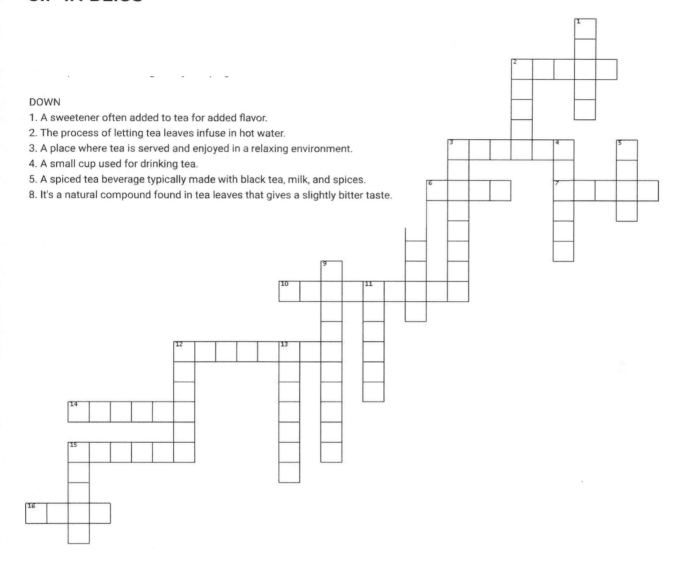

DOWN

1. A sweetener often added to tea for added flavor.
2. The process of letting tea leaves infuse in hot water.
3. A place where tea is served and enjoyed in a relaxing environment.
4. A small cup used for drinking tea.
5. A spiced tea beverage typically made with black tea, milk, and spices.
8. It's a natural compound found in tea leaves that gives a slightly bitter taste.

ACROSS

2. A delicious pastry often enjoyed with tea.
3. A vessel used for steeping and serving tea.
6. Grey A black tea flavored with bergamot oil, known for its citrusy aroma.
7. A type of black tea known for its strong and malty flavor.
10. This herbal tea is known for its calming properties.
12. A natural stimulant found in tea leaves, known for its energy-boosting effects.
14. A type of tea made from various herbs and botanicals.
15. A traditional Chinese teapot used for steeping and sipping tea.
16. The process of making tea by steeping tea leaves in hot water.

"SIP IN BLISS"

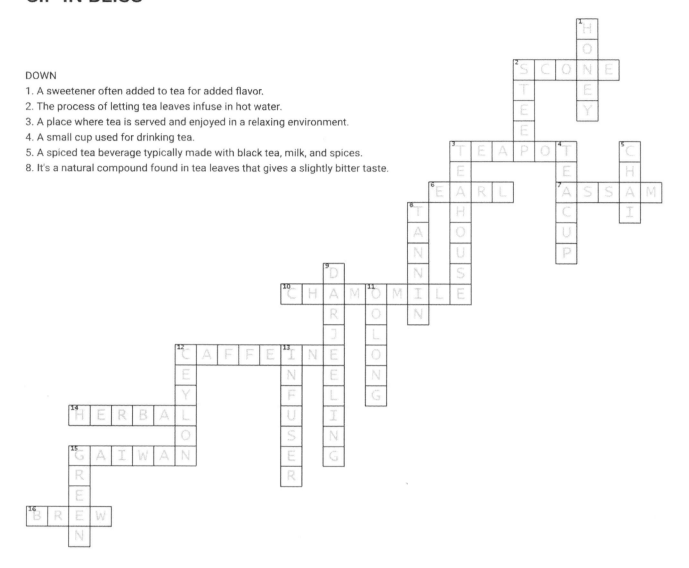

DOWN

1. A sweetener often added to tea for added flavor.
2. The process of letting tea leaves infuse in hot water.
3. A place where tea is served and enjoyed in a relaxing environment.
4. A small cup used for drinking tea.
5. A spiced tea beverage typically made with black tea, milk, and spices.
8. It's a natural compound found in tea leaves that gives a slightly bitter taste.

ACROSS

2. A delicious pastry often enjoyed with tea.
3. A vessel used for steeping and serving tea.
6. Grey A black tea flavored with bergamot oil, known for its citrusy aroma.
7. A type of black tea known for its strong and malty flavor.
10. This herbal tea is known for its calming properties.
12. A natural stimulant found in tea leaves, known for its energy-boosting effects.
14. A type of tea made from various herbs and botanicals.
15. A traditional Chinese teapot used for steeping and sipping tea.
16. The process of making tea by steeping tea leaves in hot water.

SIP IN TRANQUIL BLISS

```
G E U P E D O W N X Y M J S I
N H I I K D S O K T F Y B E P
I C Z R Z C I T I O C Q M R E
H H X U E S D L E A B V Y E U
T U Y C U V I R C E Q I O N E
O N Y F U U E I A G P Q M I C
O T N A Q G L R U Z R E T T N
S I F N W E L I X I R E D Y E
D L A R D P A B B J A V D G G
P R R U E S S I O N N O C C L
T K Y P A R E H T A M O R A U
I S B D W E R W D I J V A K D
P D E C A D E N C E I R D I N
S N O I T A N E V U J E R V I
D E B M E D I T A T I V E W T
```

Aromatherapy

Delicacy

Infusion

Reverie

Soothing

Tranquility

Connoisseur

Elixir

Meditative

Sereni

Steeped

Decadence

Indulgence

Rejuvenation

Serenity

tea

SIP IN TRANQUIL BLISS

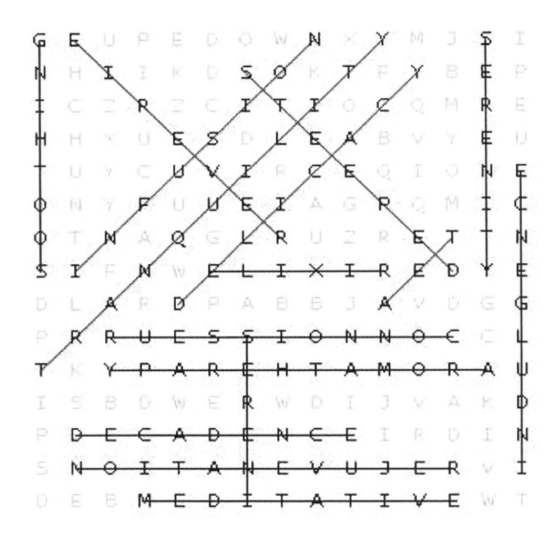

Aromatherapy	Connoisseur	Decadence
Delicacy	Elixir	Indulgence
Infusion	Meditative	Rejuvenation
Reverie	Sereni	Serenity
Soothing	Steeped	tea
Tranquility		

SIP AND FIND SERENITY

ACROSS

3. A vessel used for brewing and serving tea.

8. The act of unwinding and finding calmness, often associated with tea consumption.

9. The pleasant smell of brewed tea.

10. A state of deep focus and relaxation often achieved during tea rituals.

12. The state of calm and tranquility often associated with tea time.

16. Calming and comforting, like the experience of sipping a warm cup of tea.

17. A small cup used for drinking tea.

18. A device used to hold loose tea leaves while steeping.

DOWN

1. The process of soaking tea leaves in hot water to extract their flavors.

2. A natural stimulant found in tea leaves.

4. Used to describe a light and subtle tea flavor.

5. Having a strong, pleasant smell, like the aroma of brewed tea.

6. The delightful discovery or chance encounter of a perfect tea blend or teapot.

7. A herbal tea made from various botanical ingredients.

11. The process of extracting flavors and properties from tea leaves or herbs.

13. Describes teas that have floral notes and aromas.

14. tea A play on words that combines serenity and tea, emphasizing the calming nature of tea.

15. To prepare tea by steeping it in hot water.

16. To drink slowly and enjoy the flavors of tea.

SIP AND FIND SERENITY

ACROSS

3. A vessel used for brewing and serving tea.

8. The act of unwinding and finding calmness, often associated with tea consumption.

9. The pleasant smell of brewed tea.

10. A state of deep focus and relaxation often achieved during tea rituals.

12. The state of calm and tranquility often associated with tea time.

16. Calming and comforting, like the experience of sipping a warm cup of tea.

17. A small cup used for drinking tea.

18. A device used to hold loose tea leaves while steeping.

DOWN

1. The process of soaking tea leaves in hot water to extract their flavors.

2. A natural stimulant found in tea leaves.

4. Used to describe a light and subtle tea flavor.

5. Having a strong, pleasant smell, like the aroma of brewed tea.

6. The delightful discovery or chance encounter of a perfect tea blend or teapot.

7. A herbal tea made from various botanical ingredients.

11. The process of extracting flavors and properties from tea leaves or herbs.

13. Describes teas that have floral notes and aromas.

14. tea A play on words that combines serenity and tea, emphasizing the calming nature of tea.

15. To prepare tea by steeping it in hot water.

16. To drink slowly and enjoy the flavors of tea.

ENJOY THE SUBLIME SIP

```
S H L U F S S I L B G Z D G I
T Q J A N W N I Q N D S S N K
E J T F E F U Z I R E E M I C
M O O K U Q Q H T S L R Q T U
P H J S N S T P U S I E Z N E
T T I A C O T O L Q C N H A C
I O R H O I H E K R A I Y H N
N T U S A A T P E S C T R C E
G E N S E C N A A P Y Y E N G
P X Y T S V O V M V E X V E L
E L I X I R O X V O J D E Y U
F W Z I H R A K D S R B R V D
R U E S S I O N N O C A I G N
E V I T A T I D E M V B E E I
S O P H I S T I C A T E D N T
```

Aromatic	Blissful	Connoisseur
Delicacy	Elixir	Enchanting
Indulgence	Infusion	Meditative
Reverie	Savor	Serenity
Soothing	Sophisticated	Steeped
Teahouse	Tempting	Tranquil

ENJOY THE SUBLIME SIP

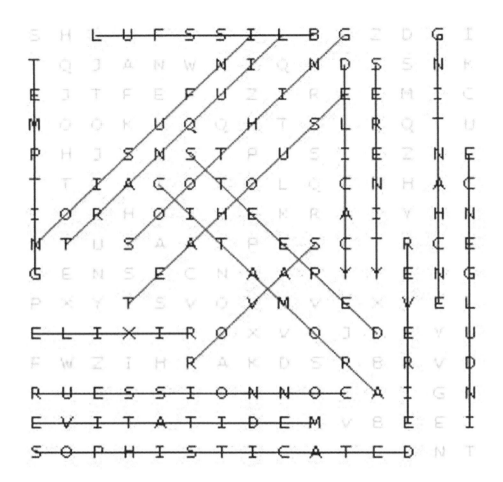

Aromatic	Blissful	Connoisseur
Delicacy	Elixir	Enchanting
Indulgence	Infusion	Meditative
Reverie	Savor	Serenity
Soothing	Sophisticated	Steeped
Teahouse	Tempting	Tranquil

Tea facts

Tea Origins: The history of tea dates back thousands of years, originating in China. According to legend, Emperor Shen Nong discovered tea when tea leaves fell into his boiling water and created a delightful infusion.

Types of Tea: There are several types of tea, including black, green, oolong, white, and herbal teas. Each type has its unique flavor profile and preparation method.

Tea and Health: Tea is known for its potential health benefits. Green tea, for example, is rich in antioxidants and is believed to have positive effects on metabolism, heart health, and brain function.

Teapots Around the World: Teapots come in various shapes, sizes, and materials. Different cultures have their own styles of teapots, such as the traditional Chinese Yixing clay teapots or the Japanese cast iron teapots called Tetsubin.

Teapots and Art: Teapots have long been celebrated as works of art. Many artists and craftsmen create intricate and unique teapot designs, often combining functionality with aesthetic beauty.

Tea facts

Teapot Materials: Teapots can be made from a variety of materials, including ceramic, porcelain, glass, stainless steel, cast iron, and more. Each material has its own qualities that affect the brewing and serving experience.

Tea Ceremonies: Tea ceremonies are traditional rituals performed in various cultures, such as the Japanese tea ceremony (Chanoyu) or the Chinese tea ceremony (Gongfu Cha). These ceremonies highlight the artistry and mindfulness involved in tea preparation and consumption.

Tea Accessories: Alongside teapots, there are several other tea accessories like tea cups, tea strainers, tea infusers, tea trays, and tea cozies. These accessories enhance the overall tea-drinking experience.

Tea Traditions: Tea has become an integral part of many cultural traditions around the world. From British afternoon tea to Moroccan mint tea, different cultures have their own unique tea customs and rituals.

Herbal Infusions: Apart from traditional tea made from the Camellia sinensis plant, there are also herbal infusions known as tisanes. These are caffeine-free beverages made from various herbs, flowers, and botanicals.

Tea Labyrinth

Tea Labyrinth

Teapot Maze Madness

Teapot Maze Madness

Brewed Pathways

Brewed Pathways

Infusion Quest

Infusion Quest

Steeped Puzzle Trails

Steeped Puzzle Trails

Tea facts

Tea Etiquette: In many cultures, there are specific etiquette and rituals associated with tea drinking. For example, in Japanese tea ceremonies, there are precise movements and gestures involved in the preparation and serving of tea.

Teapot Shapes: Teapots come in various shapes and styles, each with its own functionality and aesthetic appeal. Some common teapot shapes include classic round pots, square pots, pumpkin-shaped pots, and gourd-shaped pots.

Tea Gardens: Tea gardens are cultivated areas where tea plants are grown and harvested. These gardens can be found in countries like China, Japan, India, Sri Lanka, Kenya, and others. They offer serene environments for tea lovers to explore and appreciate tea culture.

Teapot Collecting: Teapot collecting is a popular hobby for many enthusiasts. Collectors often seek out unique and antique teapots from different periods and regions, valuing them for their historical significance and artistic craftsmanship.

Tea Blends: Apart from single-origin teas, many tea blends are created by combining different types of teas and adding other natural ingredients like herbs, flowers, and fruits. These blends offer a wide range of flavors and aromas.

Tea facts

Teapot Materials and Heat Retention: The material from which a teapot is made can affect its heat retention properties. For example, cast iron teapots are known for their excellent heat retention, while glass teapots allow for a visual appreciation of the brewing process.

Teapot Spouts: Teapot spouts are designed to provide a controlled and smooth pour. The shape and angle of the spout can influence the flow of tea and prevent dripping.

Tea Culture and Ceremonies: Different cultures have unique tea ceremonies and traditions. For instance, the British have a rich tea culture, with the tradition of afternoon tea featuring tea, scones, sandwiches, and cakes.

Tea and Well-being: Tea is often associated with relaxation and well-being. Many people find comfort in a cup of tea as it provides a moment of pause and an opportunity to unwind.

Teapot Artists: There are artists and craftsmen who specialize in creating teapots as artistic pieces. These teapots often exhibit intricate designs, elaborate details, and creative interpretations of traditional teapot forms.

This is your Hidden Message Puzzle!

```
T E A P O P I N F U S E R T C
M A G I C U E N F O H L P D O
S A W D I M I E X V A A A C L
S T O V E T O P T V N N I E L
W H I M S I C A L S D M N T E
G N I M R A H C E J A E T A C
E N A M E L E T P R N V E C T
O V R R I G A L E E T I D I I
E L E G A N T C M H G T M R B
U M S T R A I N E R B A Y T L
F S N O N A S I T R A R C N E
V I P O R C E L A I N O V I C
V E T A C I L E D W X C A I Z
H E I R L O O M T H G E I P T
E R U T A I N I M O W D M G G
```

Artisan	Ceramic	Charming
Collectible	Decorative	Delicate
Elegant	Enamel	Hand
Heirloom	Infuser	Intricate
Miniature	Ornate	painted
Porcelain	Steep	Stovetop
Strainer	Vintage	Whimsical

__ __

This puzzle is a word search puzzle that has a hidden message in it.

First find all the words in the list.

Words can go in any direction and share letters as well as cross over each other.

Once you find all the words. Copy the unused letters starting in the top left corner into the blanks to reveal the hidden message.

This is your Hidden Message Puzzle!

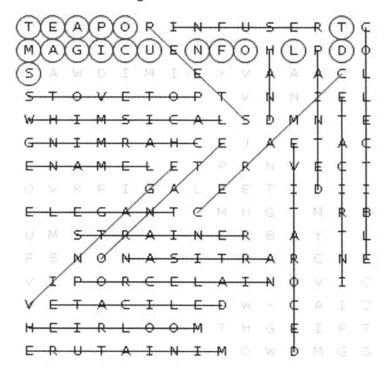

Artisan	Ceramic	Charming
Collectible	Decorative	Delicate
Elegant	Enamel	Hand
Heirloom	Infuser	Intricate
Miniature	Ornate	painted
Porcelain	Steep	Stovetop
Strainer	Vintage	Whimsical

T e a p o t M a g i c U n f o l d s

This puzzle is a word search puzzle that has a hidden message in it.

First find all the words in the list.

Words can go in any direction and share letters as well as cross over each other.

Once you find all the words. Copy the unused letters starting in the top left corner into the blanks to reveal the hidden message.

This is your Hidden Message Puzzle!

```
T  L  A  V  E  N  D  E  R  G  O  T  T  I  E
N  M  E  F  O  Y  R  O  N  T  O  E  E  A  N
I  R  K  T  E  M  O  I  E  M  L  A  L  A  I
M  A  B  R  B  I  L  L  A  H  O  H  M  A  M
N  S  G  G  B  E  I  T  I  D  N  R  C  K  S
O  S  Q  O  E  M  C  B  I  L  G  E  B  Y  A
M  A  S  J  O  H  I  K  U  R  A  E  T  Z  J
E  M  R  M  A  S  R  E  X  A  C  L  N  E  A
L  A  A  V  C  E  E  A  T  E  A  E  E  N  A
D  H  X  U  G  S  E  T  I  I  H  N  E  T  U
C  T  S  N  A  T  A  T  A  B  H  B  R  X  P
G  F  I  S  B  W  G  X  M  M  R  W  G  L  S
N  G  D  Y  R  A  H  C  N  E  S  E  I  J  S
Y  U  R  F  E  C  U  J  V  F  S  S  L  Y  H
P  O  J  V  Y  Q  X  I  A  H  C  K  T  A  R
```

Assam	Chai	Chamomile
Darjeeling	Earl	erh
Ginger	Green	Grey
Hibiscus	Jasmine	Lavender
Lemon	Matcha	mate
Mint	Oolong	Pu
Rooibos	Sencha	tea
tea	tea	tea
tea	verbena	White
Yerba		

__ __ __ __ __ __ __ __ __ __ __ __

This puzzle is a word search puzzle that has a hidden message in it.

First find all the words in the list.

Words can go in any direction and share letters as well as cross over each other.

Once you find all the words. Copy the unused letters starting in the top left corner into the blanks to reveal the hidden message.

This is your Hidden Message Puzzle!

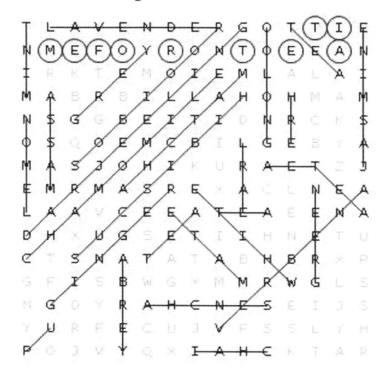

Assam	Chai	Chamomile
Darjeeling	Earl	erh
Ginger	Green	Grey
Hibiscus	Jasmine	Lavender
Lemon	Matcha	mate
Mint	Oolong	Pu
Rooibos	Sencha	tea
tea	tea	tea
tea	verbena	White
Yerba		

T i m e   f o r   t e a
___ ___ ___ ___   ___ ___ ___   ___ ___ ___

This puzzle is a word search puzzle that has a hidden message in it.

First find all the words in the list.

Words can go in any direction and share letters as well as cross over each other.

Once you find all the words. Copy the unused letters starting in the top left corner into the blanks to reveal the hidden message.

This is your Hidden Message Puzzle!

```
G G I M S O N O K S T H L O S
U E A A I E N O O E G G R T O
N N H S E A T U M N E U A R B
P M C A I T C I O E K M E U I
O A A L L H Y L H O L F U W O
W I C A O N O V Y W P E A N O
D C T N O O U G V C O I X Y R
E H G E T M J M G Y M A N L P
R A P M N S A N R H F H O F I
R A T C E N A R M A L C L R H
W H I T E S E L T R Y M Y E E
R Z Z E P B V K B D L C E T S
K N N A D W O L L E Y C C T O
W B L E N D N A C I R F A U R
L L E W N O G A R D M Q Z B R
```

African	Berry	Blast
Blend	Butterfly	Ceylon
Chai	Chai	Dragonwell
Earl	Genmaicha	Gunpowder
Gyokuro	Keemun	Lapsang
Lemon	Masala	Milk
Myrtle	Nectar	Oolong
Pea	Peony	Rooibos
Rosehip	Souchong	tea
White	White	Yellow

__ __ __ __ __ __ __ __ __ __ __ __ __ __ __ __ __

This puzzle is a word search puzzle that has a hidden message in it.

First find all the words in the list.

Words can go in any direction and share letters as well as cross over each other.

Once you find all the words. Copy the unused letters starting in the top left corner into the blanks to reveal the hidden message.

This is your Hidden Message Puzzle!

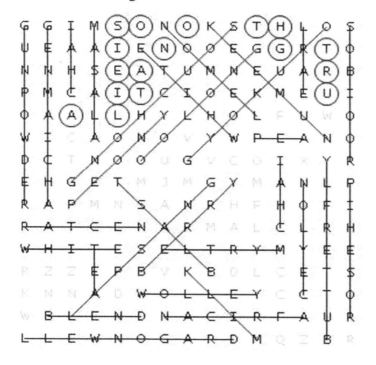

African	Berry	Blast
Blend	Butterfly	Ceylon
Chai	Chai	Dragonwell
Earl	Genmaicha	Gunpowder
Gyokuro	Keemun	Lapsang
Lemon	Masala	Milk
Myrtle	Nectar	Oolong
Pea	Peony	Rooibos
Rosehip	Souchong	tea
White	White	Yellow

S o o t h i n g   t e a   r i t u a l

This puzzle is a word search puzzle that has a hidden message in it.

First find all the words in the list.

Words can go in any direction and share letters as well as cross over each other.

Once you find all the words. Copy the unused letters starting in the top left corner into the blanks to reveal the hidden message.

This is your Hidden Message Puzzle!

```
R  S  D  Z  A  R  O  M  A  T  E  E  E  P  U
E  E  E  E  W  E  L  L  N  E  S  S  N  D  P
F  N  V  I  L  N  C  R  S  E  R  Y  A  E  L
N  R  I  I  T  I  I  A  Y  Z  T  Q  S  A  I
K  I  A  F  V  X  G  W  L  I  A  X  I  L  F
N  O  N  G  I  E  E  H  L  M  I  E  T  A  T
E  I  P  L  R  T  Q  I  T  R  I  L  H  B  I
D  N  E  L  B  A  U  Z  S  F  S  N  Q  R  N
S  P  H  L  N  Q  N  I  D  T  U  Q  G  E  G
N  R  I  X  N  E  N  T  M  B  I  L  B  H  J
O  O  Z  A  C  F  C  E  R  E  M  O  N  Y  R
C  L  R  T  U  B  R  E  W  S  O  O  T  H  E
J  T  A  S  M  E  D  I  T  A  T  I  V  E  M
I  R  E  M  G  N  I  M  A  E  T  S  W  M  V
G  D  W  G  I  D  D  C  H  H  X  Y  W  E  O
```

Aroma	Blend	Brew
Calming	Ceremony	Delightful
Elixir	Fragrant	Herbal
Infused	Meditative	Nectar
Revive	Soothe	Steaming
Tisane	Tranquility	Uplifting
Wellness	Zen	

— — — — — — — — — — — — — — — — — — — —

This puzzle is a word search puzzle that has a hidden message in it.

First find all the words in the list.

Words can go in any direction and share letters as well as cross over each other.

Once you find all the words. Copy the unused letters starting in the top left corner into the blanks to reveal the hidden message.

This is your Hidden Message Puzzle!

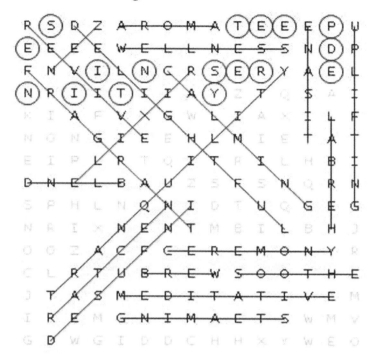

Aroma	Blend	Brew
Calming	Ceremony	Delightful
Elixir	Fragrant	Herbal
Infused	Meditative	Nectar
Revive	Soothe	Steaming
Tisane	Tranquility	Uplifting
Wellness	Zen	

S t e e p e d   i n   s e r e n i t y

This puzzle is a word search puzzle that has a hidden message in it.

First find all the words in the list.

Words can go in any direction and share letters as well as cross over each other.

Once you find all the words. Copy the unused letters starting in the top left corner into the blanks to reveal the hidden message.

Tea facts

Origin: Tea originated in ancient China and has been consumed for thousands of years. It later spread to other parts of Asia and eventually to the rest of the world.

Types of Tea: There are four main types of tea: black, green, oolong, and white. They differ in terms of processing methods and level of oxidation.

Health Benefits: Tea contains antioxidants called catechins, which have been linked to various health benefits, including improved heart health, reduced risk of certain cancers, and enhanced cognitive function.

Caffeine Content: The caffeine content in tea varies depending on the type and brewing time. On average, a cup of tea contains less caffeine than a cup of coffee, but it can still provide a gentle energy boost.

Herbal Infusions: Not all tea comes from the Camellia sinensis plant. Herbal infusions, such as chamomile, peppermint, and rooibos, are made from different herbs, flowers, and spices, offering unique flavors and potential health benefits.

Tea facts

Tea Cultures: Tea is deeply ingrained in the cultures of many countries, including China, Japan, India, the United Kingdom, Morocco, and Turkey. Each culture has its own rituals, ceremonies, and tea etiquette.

Tea and Relaxation: Tea is often associated with relaxation and mindfulness. Taking the time to prepare and enjoy a cup of tea can be a calming and meditative practice.

Tea Traditions: Tea has inspired various traditions and rituals, such as the Japanese tea ceremony, British afternoon tea, and Moroccan mint tea preparation. These traditions often emphasize hospitality, socializing, and the appreciation of tea.

Tea Production: The top tea-producing countries in the world include China, India, Kenya, Sri Lanka, and Turkey. Each region has its own unique tea varieties and processing methods.

Tea Flavors: Tea can have a wide range of flavors and aromas, from delicate and floral to bold and robust. Factors such as tea type, growing conditions, processing, and blending techniques contribute to the diverse flavors found in different teas.

This is your Fallen Phrase Puzzle!

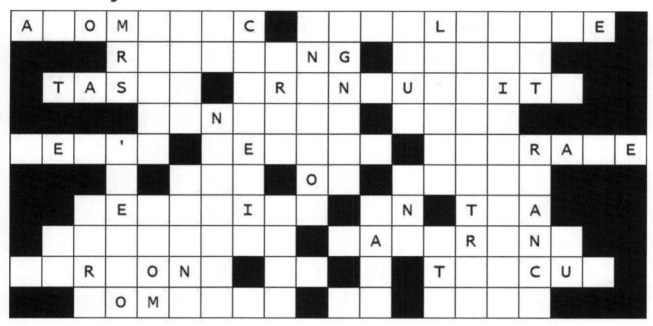

Try to rebuild the message.

The letters from each cell are below the puzzle.

Try to rebuild the original message by choosing the letters for each cell.

This is your Fallen Phrase Puzzle!

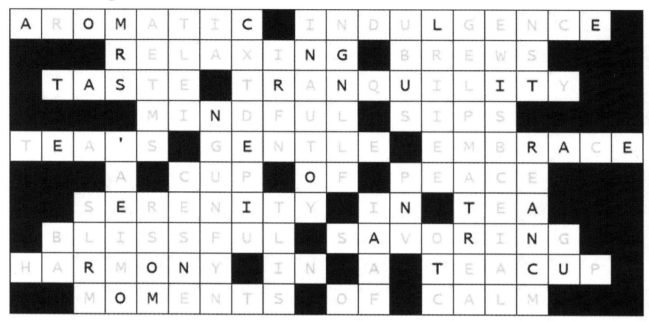

Try to rebuild the message.

The letters from each cell are below the puzzle.
Try to rebuild the original message by choosing the letters for each cell.

This is your Fallen Phrase Puzzle!

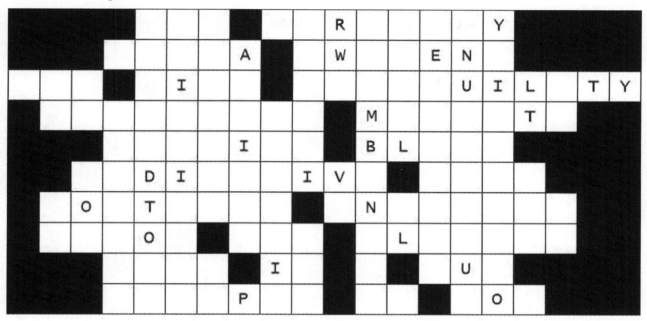

Try to rebuild the message.

The letters from each cell are below the puzzle.

Try to rebuild the original message by choosing the letters for each cell.

This is your Fallen Phrase Puzzle!

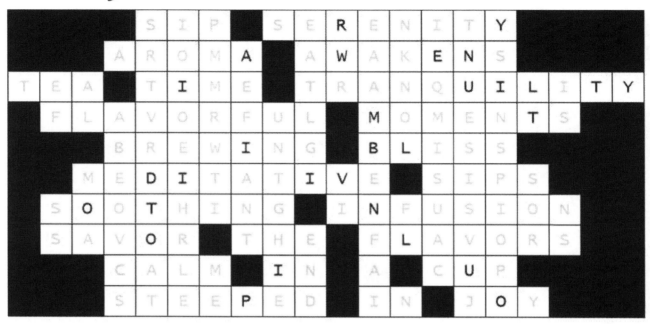

			S	I	P		S	E	R	E	N	I	T	Y			
			A	R	O	M	A		A	W	A	K	E	N	S		
T	E	A		T	I	M	E		T	R	A	N	Q	U	I	L	I	T	Y
	F	L	A	V	O	R	F	U	L		M	O	M	E	N	T	S	
		B	R	E	W	I	N	G		B	L	I	S	S	
	M	E	D	I	T	A	T	I	V	E		S	I	P	S	
S	O	O	T	H	I	N	G		I	N	F	U	S	I	O	N
S	A	V	O	R		T	H	E		F	L	A	V	O	R	S
	C	A	L	M		I	N		A		C	U	P	
	S	T	E	E	P	E	D		I	N		J	O	Y

```
                    T
        A       R   P           D               C
        O   T   O   M       G   N       E       A   S   O
        V   V   O   M       E   A       F   N   S   I   S
        A   R   L   I   A   U   G       I   K   Q   E   P
    F   L   E   T   E   W   E   T       A   N   M   V   I   Y   S
    E   M   B   A   H   M   N   H   L   A   F   I   J   P   R   I
    S   A   S   S   E   R   F   S   T   I   E   O   I   S   N   S   N
T   S   A   C   R   I   E   T   N   E   R   A   N   U   T   S   O   S
```

Try to rebuild the message.

The letters from each cell are below the puzzle.
Try to rebuild the original message by choosing the letters for each cell.

This is your Fallen Phrase Puzzle!

		W		R		T										
			E					E								
		T			G											
				O								L				
				E			S		D							
	F		S							R						
			P													
T		'					E									
				I						C						

```
                H
                U                                      I
                M           N  T  O         E  U  C  I  O
       E  I  M           N  T  L  U      A  A  N  M  I
       N  T     M  S  H  V  E  S      Q  E  N  R  E  T
    O  A     S     L  E  N  T  E  F      S  B  B  R  S  O  E
    L  T     A     A  O  A  E  R  N  N  W  Y  L  P  A  T  N
 B  I  O  E  A  I  N  F  P  T  R  O  N  H  A  M  U  H  S  Y
 T  E  A  N  W  H  I  E  N  D  R  A  F  S  M  I  C  P  C  S
 S  E  A  S  D  O  G  A  S  E  I  A  N  A  D  E  D  E  N  Y  Y
```

Try to rebuild the message.

The letters from each cell are below the puzzle.
Try to rebuild the original message by choosing the letters for each cell.

This is your Fallen Phrase Puzzle!

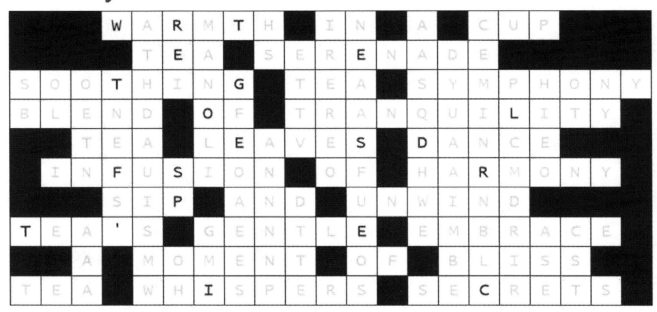

		W	A	R	M	T	H		I	N		A		C	U	P		
		T	E	A			S	E	R	E	N	A	D	E				
S	O	O	T	H	I	N	G		T	E	A		S	Y	M	P	H	O	N	Y
B	L	E	N	D		O	F		T	R	A	N	Q	U	I	L	I	T	Y
	T	E	A		L	E	A	V	E	S		D	A	N	C	E		
	I	N	F	U	S	I	O	N		O	F		H	A	R	M	O	N	Y
	S	I	P		A	N	D		U	N	W	I	N	D			
T	E	A	'	S		G	E	N	T	L	E		E	M	B	R	A	C	E
		A		M	O	M	E	N	T		O	F		B	L	I	S	S
T	E	A		W	H	I	S	P	E	R	S		S	E	C	R	E	T	S

```
            H
            U                                    I
            M         N  T  O        E  U  C  I  O
      E     I    M    N  T  L  U     A  A  N  M  I
      N     T    M  S  H  V  E  S    Q  E  N  R  E  T
   O  A     S    L  E  N  T  E  F    S  B  B  R  S  O  E
   L  T     A    A  O  A  E  R  N  N  W  Y  L  P  A  T  N
B  I  O  E  A  I  N  F  P  T  R  O  N  H  A  M  U  H  S  Y
T  E  A  N  W  H  I  E  N  D  R  A  F  S  M  I  C  P  C  S
S  E  A  S  D  O  G  A  S  E  I  A  N  A  D  E  D  E  N  Y  Y
```

Try to rebuild the message.

The letters from each cell are below the puzzle.
Try to rebuild the original message by choosing the letters for each cell.

Tea facts

Tea Varieties: Apart from the four main types of tea (black, green, oolong, and white), there are also specialty teas such as matcha (powdered green tea), Pu-erh (fermented tea), and blooming teas (handcrafted tea balls that unfurl in hot water).

Tea Origins: Tea originated in China, and the Camellia sinensis plant was first cultivated in the Yunnan province. From there, tea cultivation and consumption spread to other regions, including India, Japan, Sri Lanka, and Taiwan.

Tea and Health: Tea contains beneficial compounds like polyphenols and catechins that have antioxidant and anti-inflammatory properties. Regular tea consumption has been associated with potential health benefits such as improved heart health, reduced risk of certain cancers, and enhanced brain function.

Herbal Infusions: While herbal infusions are commonly referred to as "herbal teas," technically, they are not true teas as they do not come from the Camellia sinensis plant. Herbal infusions are made by steeping herbs, flowers, fruits, or spices in hot water.

Tea Traditions: Many cultures around the world have unique tea traditions. For example, the Japanese tea ceremony (known as "chado" or "sado") is a highly ritualized and meditative practice. In Morocco, mint tea is a symbol of hospitality and is traditionally prepared and served with elaborate gestures.

Tea facts

Terroir Influence: Similar to wine, the flavors and characteristics of tea can be influenced by the terroir—the environmental conditions, altitude, soil, and climate in which the tea is grown. This can give teas from different regions distinct flavors and profiles.

Tea Accessories: Tea culture is often accompanied by a variety of specialized accessories. These may include teapots, teacups, tea trays, tea infusers, tea strainers, tea scoops, and tea storage containers.

Tea Etiquette: Different cultures have their own tea etiquettes. For instance, in Japan, it is customary to bow when receiving or serving tea, and in British afternoon tea, there are specific rules about how to hold the teacup and stir the tea.

Tea and Meditation: Tea has been used as a focal point for meditation and mindfulness practices. The process of preparing and drinking tea can be a mindful experience, encouraging presence and a sense of calm.

Tea and Pairings: Tea can be paired with various foods to enhance flavors and create harmonious combinations. For example, green tea is often paired with sushi, black tea with chocolate, and oolong tea with roasted nuts.

Tea is a fascinating and diverse subject with a rich history and cultural significance. Exploring the world of tea can lead to an appreciation for its flavors, traditions, and the soothing moments it brings. Enjoy your journey into the delightful realm of tea!

Printed in Great Britain
by Amazon

35085373R00057